# The
# Story of Ruth

## By REV. JUDE WINKLER, OFM Conv.

**Imprimi Potest: Daniel Pietrzak, OFM Conv.,** Minister Provincial of St. Anthony of Padua Province (USA)
**Nihil Obstat: Daniel V. Flynn, J.C.D.,** Censor Librorum
**Imprimatur: Patrick J. Sheridan,** Vicar General, Archdiocese of New York

## Naomi travels to Moab

WHEN the Israelites entered the Promised Land, they were filled with great hope for it was a land flowing with milk and honey. Yet, there were years in which the rains did not fall and when the people had very little to eat.

These times of famine were very difficult for the Israelites because they did not have any powerful leaders who could guide the nation through the crisis. Moses and Joshua had died long ago and they did not yet have the kings. Their leaders were the Judges who did not have the power to bring the people together to help each other.

It was during one of these famines that the family of a woman named Naomi left their home in Bethlehem to try to find food. Naomi was married to a man named Elimelech and they had two sons, Mahlon and Chilion.

This family traveled to a foreign land, the land of Moab. The people of Israel hated the people of Moab for they were pagans and the Moabites hated the Israelites. Yet Naomi and her family were able to settle there and earn a living.

## Mahlon and Chilion marry Moabite women

IT was rare for Israelites even to talk with Moabites, but Naomi's family had no choice—it was a question of life and death.

While they were living in Moab, her two sons reached the age at which Israelites would normally marry. In Israel they would naturally have married Israelite women, but there were none around in Moab. So Mahlon and Chilion married Moabite women. Their wives were Ruth and Orpah, and both of them were good and kind women.

## Naomi is left alone

BUT Naomi's misfortune did not end with her having to leave her native land. Just before her sons had married, her husband, Elimelech, had died, leaving her a widow. Yet, her two sons took care of their mother.

Then, about ten years after they had moved to Moab, both of her sons died. She was all alone in the world except for two daughters-in-law, but they were Moabites and were still pagans.

There was no one whom she could really trust to take care of her when she became old or if she became sick. She could not count on any help from the Moabites, for she was a foreigner and a member of a nation that they hated.

## Naomi decides to go back home

NAOMI decided that the best thing for her to do was to return to her homeland, to the city of Bethlehem.

She called her two daughters-in-law and spoke with them. She really loved them and wanted to do what was best for them, so she decided that it would be unfair for her to take them with her. She knew what it was like to be a foreigner living in a land where one was hated, and she didn't want to force that upon Ruth and Orpah.

Naomi told her daughters-in-law that they should go home to their parents' houses. She knew that these women were still young and their parents could arrange for them to be married. This way they could live out their lives in their own land and with families of their own. It would mean that Naomi would be all alone in the world, but at least her daughters-in-law would have a decent life.

Orpah loved Naomi but she knew that her mother-in-law was right. She wept with her for a while and then kissed her and went on her way. But Ruth refused to give up. She held on to Naomi and would not let go.

7

## Ruth promises Naomi her love

RUTH told Naomi that she would never return to her family. She would go wherever Naomi would go. Naomi's people would be her own people and Naomi's God would be her God. She swore an oath to God that she would never abandon her mother-in-law.

Naomi realized that Ruth was a truly brave and loving woman. She knew that she would never convince Ruth to go home, so she kept her peace. She and Ruth would travel to Bethlehem.

This must have been a great consolation to Naomi to see how much Ruth loved her and to know that she would take care of her.

## Naomi is called Mara

WHEN Naomi and Ruth finally arrived in Bethlehem, everyone living there was surprised to see them. Naomi had moved away about ten years before, and the people there thought that they would never see her again.

Naomi's friends and relatives came up to greet her. They called her Naomi and she responded that she should really change her name. She should be called Mara which means bitter, for her life had become very bitter.

Naomi told her family and friends that she had gone away with a husband and two sons and she had returned without them.

## Life in Bethlehem

NAOMI and Ruth settled in Bethlehem. There were not many ways that a woman could earn a living in Israel in those days. Their husbands were supposed to provide for them.

When a woman became a widow, she was totally dependent upon her children. If she had no children, she was completely alone. Yet, there was one practice that was intended to answer the needs that widows and orphans would face: gleaning.

When the harvesters would go out to the fields of grain, they would cut down the wheat and barley by hand. As they were walking along, they would always miss a bit of the grain. The law was clear that they were not to go back and pick up that grain. They were to leave it so that the widows and orphans could collect it (glean it) for their needs.

The same was true of the harvesting of grapes and olives—they were to leave some of the fruit on the vines and the trees for the poor.

And so Naomi sent Ruth out to the barley fields, for the harvest had begun. She was to glean the fields after the men who were cutting the grain so that she and Naomi might have something to eat.

## Ruth gleans in Boaz's field

THERE was a certain man named Boaz who lived in Bethlehem. He owned fields outside of the city and when the harvest began, he went out to make sure that everything was going well. He had hired a number of men to do this work, and he wanted to be sure they were working.

Ruth had gone out to one of the fields owned by Boaz and she had begun to glean the grain. It was hard work, but Ruth was ready to do whatever work was needed to supply her needs and those of her mother-in-law.

She was busy working there when Boaz came out to visit that field.

# Boaz asks about Ruth

BOAZ noticed Ruth immediately, for there was something different about her. He called over his servant who was in charge of the harvesters and asked him who she was.

The servant told Boaz that she was the Moabite woman who had returned with Naomi. She had come out to him earlier and had asked him permission to glean in the field. He had said that she could, for she appeared to be a good and generous woman.

Ruth had come out to that field early that morning, the servant explained, and had worked all day without even taking a break.

## Boaz speaks with Ruth

BOAZ was so impressed with the generosity of this woman that he called Ruth over so that he could speak with her. He realized that it could be dangerous for a young woman to be working in a field filled with hired men.

Boaz assured Ruth that he had told all of them to respect her and to treat her with dignity. He told her that she should not go off to glean in other fields. She was to remain there. She could even drink from the jars of water that the young men had drawn.

Ruth was confused and she asked him why he was being so kind to her. After all, she was a foreigner.

Boaz answered that he had heard of all the good things that she had done for Naomi. The Lord would surely reward her, he said, for her goodness. He would give her a home in Israel.

At mealtime, Boaz called Ruth over again and gave her some of his bread and wine. She ate until she was filled and returned to her work. Boaz then called over some of the workmen and told them to drop some of the grain they were collecting so that she could glean it.

# Ruth returns home with the grain

RUTH continued to work in the fields all day long. Then, in the evening, she separated the grain from the stalks. She had collected almost a bushel of barley which was a very good amount for a day of gleaning.

When she finished this task, she took her grain back to the city and showed it to Naomi. She also gave her some of the food that Boaz had given her.

Naomi was very pleased with all that she saw and she asked Ruth where she had gleaned that day. Naomi said that the man who had been so kind to her should be blessed by the Lord.

"The man's name was Boaz," answered Ruth. This answer gladdened Naomi all the more, and she blessed the Lord for he was one of their relatives. She knew that Ruth would be safe working in Boaz's fields.

So Ruth continued to return to his fields, gleaning first of all during the barley harvest and then during the wheat harvest. Thus, she earned a living for herself and for her mother-in-law.

## A husband for Ruth

WHEN the harvests were over, Naomi told Ruth that it was now time for them to find her a husband.

In Israel, when a man died without having borne a son, the next male relative was supposed to marry the widow and bear a son for the man who had died. Usually this was the man's brother, but in Ruth's case, since her brother-in-law was also dead, it would have to be a cousin.

Naomi told Ruth that since Boaz was one of their relatives, she should go to visit him and ask him to be her husband.

## Ruth lies down at Boaz's feet

NAOMI told Ruth to visit Boaz and to wait until he had eaten his meal. Then, when he was finished and had gone to sleep, she should go over and lie at his feet.

So Ruth bathed and anointed herself with oil and put on her best clothes. She then went down to the place where Boaz was staying during the harvest.

She watched as Boaz ate and drank. When he had finished, he went to lie down on a pile of grain. Ruth was very careful to see where he was and when she was sure that he was asleep, she went over to him and lay down at his feet.

# Ruth asks Boaz to marry her

IN the middle of the night, Boaz woke up and saw a woman lying at his feet. He was very confused and asked her, "Who are you?"

Ruth answered, "I am Ruth, your servant." She asked him to take her as a wife for he was her relative.

Boaz was very happy when he heard this. He had liked Ruth since the first day he had seen her. He had hoped that she would want to marry him, but he was sure that she would try to marry a younger man.

He told Ruth that she would truly be blessed for asking him to be her husband for that was surely the kindest thing that she had ever done— even kinder than all the things that she had done for Naomi.

There was only one problem that they would have to solve. Boaz was not really her closest relative for there was one other man living in Bethlehem who was a closer relative than he. He told her to stay with him that night and the next morning they would speak with him and work it out.

# The next morning

THE next morning Boaz awoke very early. He asked all the men not to tell anyone that Ruth had slept there that night.

He told Ruth that she must take some grain for herself and for Naomi. He said that it would not be right for him to send her back empty-handed. So he took Ruth's mantle and measured out six measures of grain.

Ruth brought this gift back to Naomi and told her everything that Boaz had said and done. Naomi knew that this was a very good sign, and she told Ruth that she was sure that Boaz would solve everything that very day.

Boaz went down to the city where the elders used to gather. This was the place where most of the important city business took place during ancient times. Boaz saw Ruth's relative passing by and called him over.

Boaz told him that he had something important to say to him and asked him to sit down there. He then asked ten of the elders to sit down also so that they could be witnesses to everything that he was about to say and do.

## At the city gate

BOAZ told Ruth's relative that Naomi, his relative, had returned from Moab and was trying to sell the land that had belonged to Elimelech, her husband.

In Israel, a person could not sell one's land to someone outside of the family, for God Himself had assigned each family to its own land. If a man were to die and there were no sons, one of the other relatives would have to buy the land from the widow.

So Boaz told Ruth's relative that since he was the next living relative, it was his choice of whether he would buy the land or not. The man told Boaz that he would, in fact, be willing to buy the land.

Boaz then told the man that if he bought the land, he would also be required to marry Ruth, for this was the law. The man realized that he could not possibly do this, for while he had enough money to buy the land, he did not have enough to support another wife. (In those days a man could have more than one wife if he could support her and their children.)

# Boaz promises to marry Ruth

AS a sign that he was giving up his right to marry Ruth, the man took off his sandal and gave it to Boaz. In this way he was saying before all the witnesses that Boaz now had the right to marry her.

Boaz then proclaimed that he would marry Ruth so that she could have a child. This child would be considered to be the child of her first husband. In this way, there would be someone who would bear his name in Israel.

Boaz also bought the land that belonged to Naomi so that his son would inherit this land. In this way, the land which had belonged to Ruth's first husband would go to the boy who would bear his name (the son of Boaz and Ruth).

All the elders who were sitting there said that they would be witnesses to all that Boaz had said and done. They then prayed for God's blessing to come upon them.

For Ruth they prayed that she would become like Rachel and Leah, the wives of Jacob, who built up the house of Israel. For Boaz they prayed that his house would be like that of Perez, one of his ancestors.

# Ruth and Boaz marry

B OAZ then took Ruth to his home and she became his wife. She who had once given up everything in order to take care of her mother-in-law was now rewarded by God in being given a loving husband.

And the Lord continued to bless Ruth and Boaz. She became pregnant and bore a son. They named the child Obed.

Naomi was beside herself with joy when she heard that Ruth had borne a son. She blessed the Lord for He had not forgotten her and her family. He had given her a grandson who would continue to carry the name of her family.

She continued to give thanks to the Lord for now there was someone to take care of her and Ruth in their old age. She said that Ruth was worth more than seven sons and that her love was the most precious gift that she had ever received.

The birth of this child changed Naomi for she was now filled with joy. She who had once asked to be called Mara (bitter) was now overflowing with gratitude and rejoicing.

# The lesson of the story of Ruth

THE people of Israel loved to tell the story of Ruth to each other. It was a wonderful story where everything ended up well. Ruth, who was a good and generous woman, was rewarded by the Lord and given a husband, a child, and a new home. Even more than that, she was given the protection of the God Whom she had chosen to follow.

The story was important for the Israelites for another reason as well. The Israelites tended to hate the Moabites and would treat them very poorly. They thought that God hated the Moabites as well. They wouldn't think of doing a favor for a Moabite.

The story of Ruth taught them that one should not judge others by the nation from which they come or the color of their skin or their religion. God loves and cares for all people. He loved Ruth the Moabite just as much as He loved Naomi the Israelite and cared for both of them. We should be like God.

Furthermore, there was the lesson that women can be just as good and generous and courageous as men. Ruth was not a weak and frail person. She showed a strength that few men had ever shown and she served God and her neighbor in a heroic manner.

Besides these reasons, there was one last reason for the Israelites to marvel at the story of Ruth. Her son, Obed, was to be the father of a man named Jesse who was the father of David. David was to become the greatest king in the history of Israel.

One would think that a great king would have the perfect parents and grandparents. Instead, what does David have: a great-grandmother who was from a nation that Israel hated.

God doesn't look at the blood line or the color of one's skin—He looks at one's heart as He did with David, as He did with Ruth.

Dear Parents,

The Book of Ruth offers us a number of valuable lessons about God and how He interacts with His people. One example is the question of bravery. Ruth lived in an era in which bravery was usually measured by the number of deaths one was able to extract from the enemy. She challenges that picture for she was undoubtedly a brave woman. She left her family and nation, even her own gods, so that she might follow Naomi and serve her needs. Ruth never asked herself who would take care of her in her old age. She risked all to do what was right.

Another example is the whole question of the role of women in this book. Throughout most of the Old Testament, women are an afterthought. Here is a book in which the protagonist is a woman.

Still another example is the opposition to racial prejudice. The Israelites hated the Moabites, and this book told the nation that God loved all people no matter what their color or nationality or even their religion.

Finally, many of the stories of the Old Testament are filled with great miracles such as the parting of the Red Sea or the defeat of large armies of enemies. This book is unusual for it presents a story in which God works in and through the charity of people and not in an extraordinary manner. This difference is almost refreshing for it makes the book easily applicable to our everyday life.

And so, the Book of Ruth is remarkably modern. It speaks to us and challenges us to be more like this heroic woman and to be more like the God in Whom she came to believe.

Shalom,

Fr. Jude Winkler, OFM Conv.